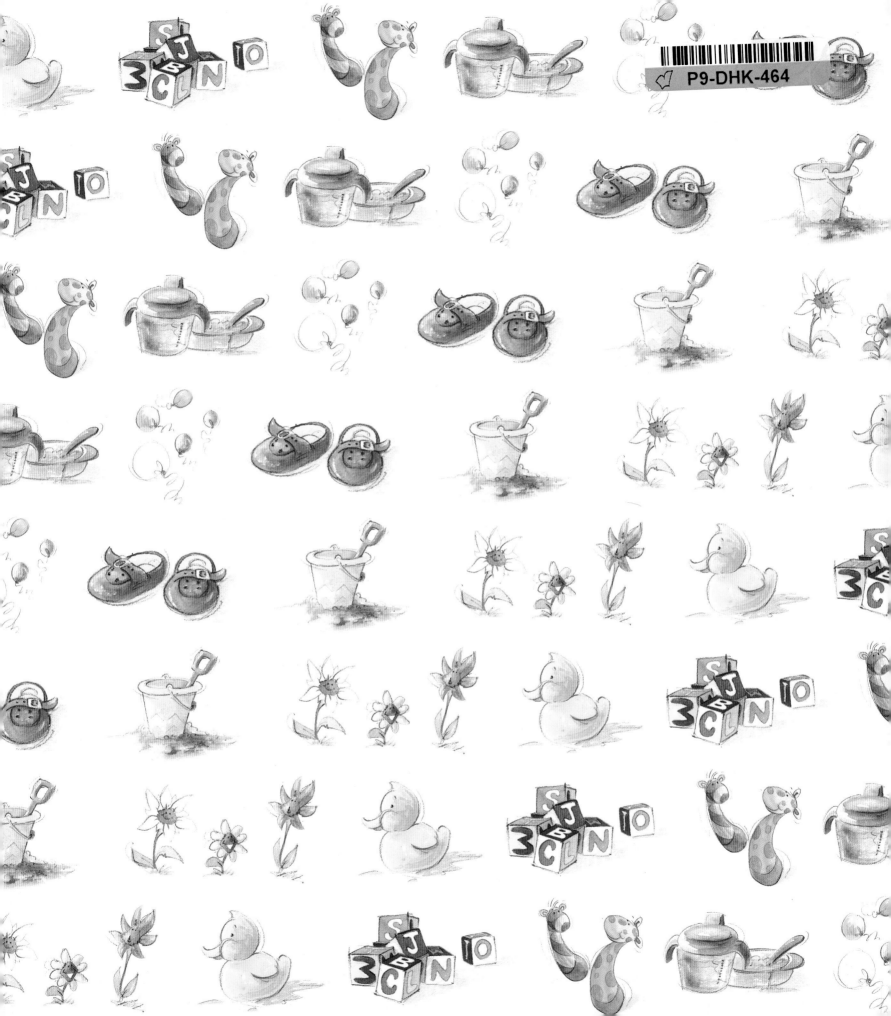

This edition 2006

First published in 2006 by Igloo Books Ltd
Garrard Way, Kettering NN16 8TD
www.igloo-books.com

Copyright © Igloo Books Ltd 2006

ISBN: 1-84561-367-8

Cover and contents illustrations by Martin Impey
Text by Rebecca Gee

Designed by seagulls

Printed in China

My Baby Record Book

My *name is* ....

And I was born on ....

My parents
before I was born

My Mother's name is ....

Her age when she was expecting me was ....

My Father's name is ....

His age when he was expecting me was ....

This is how my parents met ....

Family tree

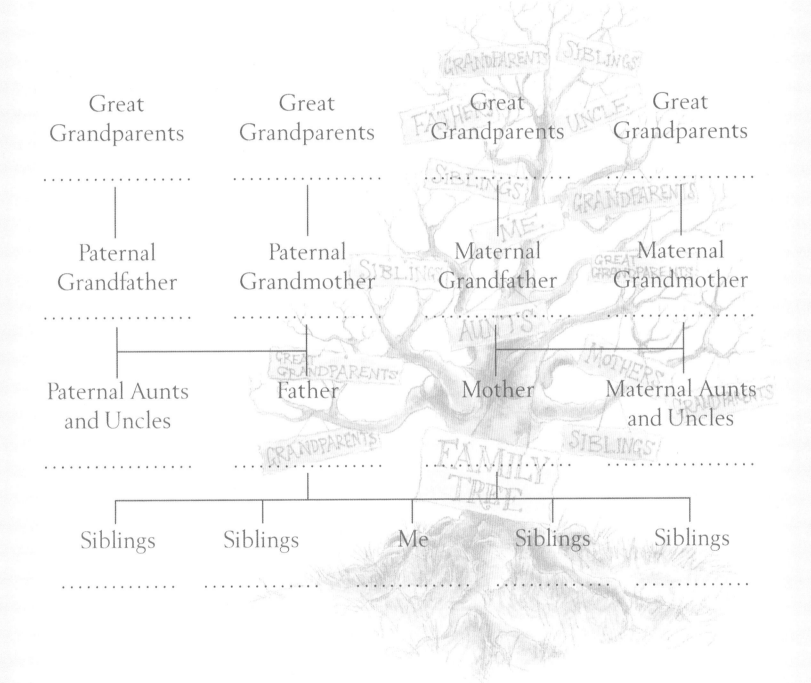

Great Grandparents Great Grandparents Great Grandparents Great Grandparents

Paternal Grandfather Paternal Grandmother Maternal Grandfather Maternal Grandmother

Paternal Aunts and Uncles Father Mother Maternal Aunts and Uncles

Siblings Siblings Me Siblings Siblings

Waiting for me

My Mother's feelings when she found out I was on the way

. . . .

My Father's feelings when he found out I was on the way

. . . .

The foods my Mother craved were

. . . .

I was due on . . . .

This is my first baby scan picture

My mother when she was pregnant with me

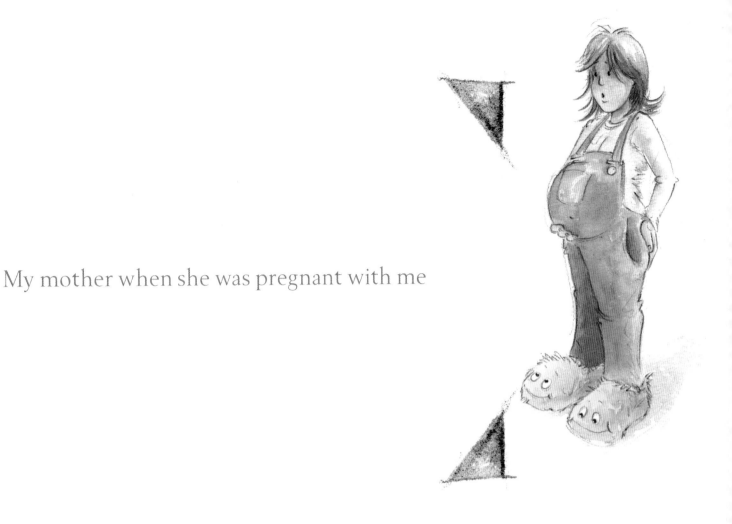

Girls' names my parents considered

....

Boys' names my parents considered

....

My parents' feelings just before my birth

....

....

Here I am!

I was born at (time)

. . . .

The place I was born was

. . . .

My eye color was . . . .

I look like . . . .   My hair was . . . .

My weight was

. . . .

My length was

. . . .

My first picture

Here is my hospital bracelet

My birth lasted ....

The midwife's name was ....

My name was chosen because ....

My parents' comments about the birth
....

....

My parents' first impressions of me
....

....

The world when I was born

The President was . . . .

Number one in the charts was

. . . .

Blockbuster films were

. . . .

A carton of milk cost . . . .

A newspaper cost . . . .   My first diapers cost . . . .

Fashions of the day were . . . .

. . . .

. . . .

Famous people who share
my birthday are

. . . .

. . . .

Historical events that happened
on my birthday are . . . .

. . . .

Here are some newspaper clippings from the day I was born

Welcome home

I came home on ....

Who brought me home

....

Who was waiting for me at home

....

My address is ....

....

....

The first thing I did when I got
home was ....

The first thing my parents did when they got home was

....

On my first night I went to sleep at

. . . .

And woke up at

. . . .

How I fed in the first week . . . .

. . . .

How I slept in the first week . . . .

. . . .

How my parents
felt in the first week

. . . .

. . . .

. . . .

. . . .

. . . .

My visitors and presents

Here is a list of all my visitors and presents in the first few weeks

. . . .

. . . .

. . . .

. . . .

. . . .

. . . .

. . . .

My hand and footprints

My hand and footprints at .... weeks

Early outings

For my first trip out I went to

....

The date was ....

This is how long it took to get me ready

....

Who took me ....

My reaction was ....

Here is a picture of me on my first outing

My stroller looked like ....

My stroller was given to me by ....

My first car ride was on .... with ....

What I thought of the car ....

My first train ride was on .... with ....

This is what happened ....

I first went on a plane on .... with ....

This is what happened ....

A picture of me on the move

Yum, yum

The first time I ate solid food was ....

What I ate ....

Who fed it to me ....

What I thought of it ....

I first tried finger foods ....

I first fed myself ....

I first used a training cup ....

I first sat in a high chair ....

My favorite foods are

....

....

And I particularly hate ....

....

Here is my messiest picture

Playtime

The person who makes me laugh the most is . . . .
because . . . .

. . . .

My best friend is . . . .

. . . .

Age . . . .

We met because . . . .

. . . .

Here's what we think of each other

. . . .

Some of the things we've done together are . . . .

. . . .

Here's a picture of us together

The first time I went to the park was on ....

What I thought of it ....

My favorite game is ....

My favorite toys are ....

The strangest thing I like playing with is ....

Look what I can do!

I first lifted my head whilst lying on my front ....

I first smiled ....

I first laughed ....

I first reached for a toy ....

I first rolled from my front to my back ....

I first sat with support ....

I first sat without support ....

I first passed an object from one hand to the other ....

I first clapped my hands ....

	DATE	AGE
I first crawled	....	....
I first started understanding words	....	....
My first word was	....	
I first pulled myself up	....	....
I first walked with a push along toy	....	....
I first walked alone	....	....

Splash!

I was given my first bath on .... by ....

My reaction ....

I first went in the big bath ....

My favorite bath games were ....
....

What I think of having my hair washed ....

The first time I went in a baby pool was ....

Where it was ....

Here's what I thought of it ....

I first went swimming on .... with ....

My reaction ....

How long I slept for afterwards! ....

Bedtime

My bedtime routine ....

....

My favorite place to sleep is ....

I can't sleep without

....

....

....

My favorite lullabies

....

....

....

....

....

24

I first slept in a crib ....

I first slept through the night ....

I first slept in a bed ....

This is how I slept ....

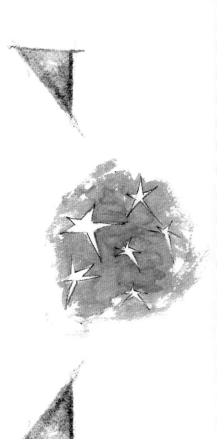

My first celebrations

Celebration ....

We celebrated on ....

The outfit I wore was ....

The people who celebrated with me were ....

This is what happened and what I thought of it all

....

Here's a picture of me celebrating with ....

Celebration ....

We celebrated on ....

The outfit I wore was ....

The people who celebrated with me were

....

This is what happened and what I thought of it all

....

Here's a picture of me celebrating with ....

My first Christmas

My age was ....

Where I spent my first Christmas ....

Who I spent it with

....

My Christmas outfit was

....

For my first
Christmas dinner I ate

....

The number one song at Christmas

was ....

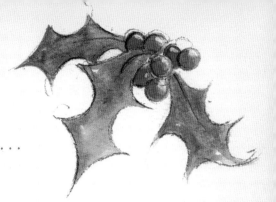

The weather was ....

A list of some of my presents

....

....

....

....

What I thought of the day ....

....

My first vacation

The date of my first vacation was ....

Where I went ....

Who came with me ....

How we got there ....

Here is a picture of me on vacation with ....

30

What I thought of the journey ....

This is how I slept on vacation ....

What the weather was like ....

The things I liked eating on vacation were

....

The thing I hated most
about my vacation was

....

....

Here are some of the things
I did on my vacation

....

....

....

....

My health

My pediatrician's name ....

What happened at my review at 6–8 weeks ....
....

What happened at my review at 6–9 months ....
....

The immunizations I received ....

This is how I reacted to my immunizations ....

My first illness was when I was .... The illness was ....

This is how I coped when I got sick ....

This is how my parents coped when I got sick! ....

My Teeth

The person who found my first tooth was

....

How I slept when I was teething

....

Other reactions when I was teething ....

First tooth appeared ....

2nd	8th	14th ....
3rd	9th	15th ....
4th	10th	16th ....
5th	11th	17th ....
6th	12th	18th ....
7th	13th	19th ....

Last tooth appeared ....

Other favorites and firsts

My favorite people are ....

What I like doing with them ....

My favorite first words were ....

....

My favorite nursery rhymes are ....

I had my first haircut on ....

The hairdresser's name was ....

This is how I reacted ....

I got my first pair of shoes on ....

This is how I reacted ....

Here is a lock of hair from my first haircut

The first time my parents went out without me was ....

They went to ....

They stayed out for ....

My babysitter was ....

This is how I behaved ....

35

As I grow

A picture of me at 3 months old

Weight .... Length .... Eye color .... Hair ....

How I was feeding .... How I was sleeping ....

The best things I've learned to do ....

....

A picture of me at 6 months old

Weight .... Length .... Eye color .... Hair ....

How I was feeding .... How I was sleeping ....

The best things I've learned to do ....

....

A picture of me at 9 months old

Weight .... Length .... Eye color .... Hair ....

How I was feeding .... How I was sleeping ....

The best things I've learned to do ....

....

A picture of me at 12 months old

Weight .... Length .... Eye color .... Hair ....

How I was feeding .... How I was sleeping ....

The best things I've learned to do ....

....

My first birthday

Who I celebrated with ....

What we did on the day ....

My first birthday cake was ....

Some of the presents I received ....

....

My parents' feelings about my first year

....
....
....
....

Plans for the future ....

What my parents think I will be when I grow up

....
....
....

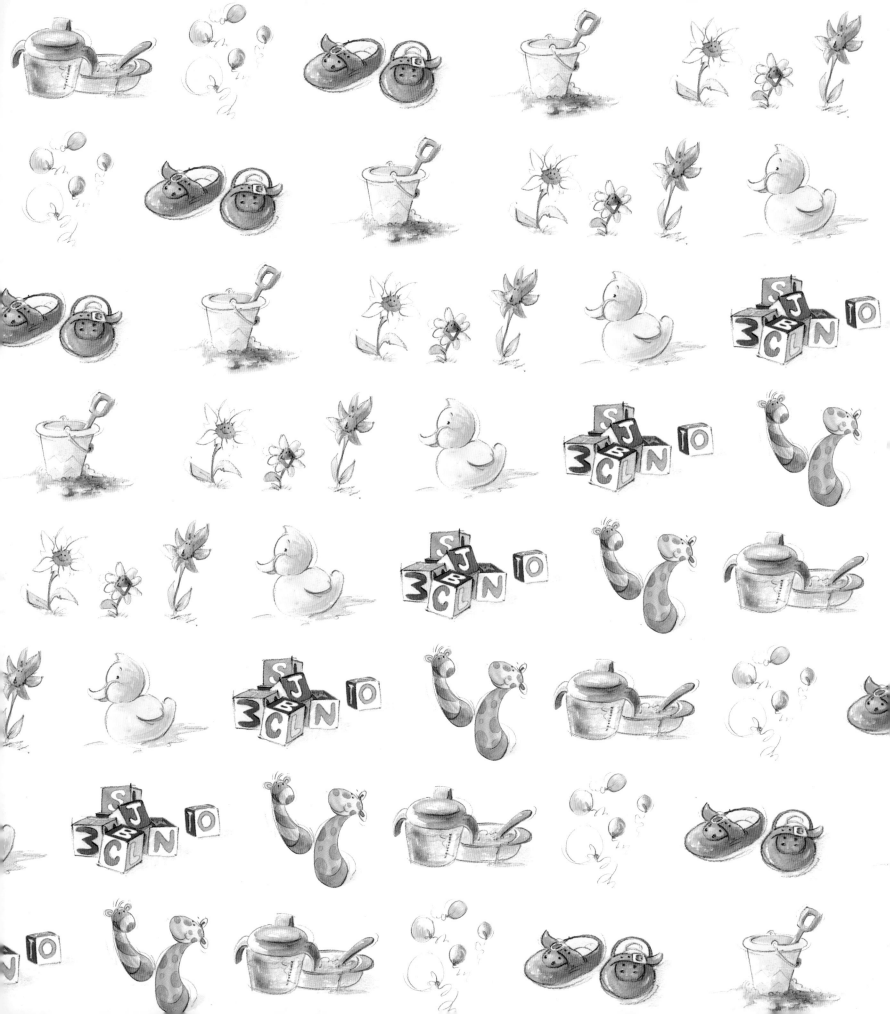